JOAN NICOLE PRINCE HOME

Living with the Dying
THE JOURNEY OF A COMFORT HOME

From:
Schenectady Community Home Inc.
Joan Nicole Prince Home

Dedicated to providing a safe, comfortable, caring
residence for terminally ill patients in need of a home
during their final days.

Schenectady Community Home Inc.

Joan Nicole Prince Home

22 Glenview Drive

Scotia, NY 12302

518-346-5471

www.joannicoleprincehome.org

FIRST EDITION

CREDITS:

Cover photo and images taken by author,
Amanda Neveu, at the Joan Nicole Prince Home

Logo created by James Lewis-Van Vorst

Editing and Guidance provided by Stacey Bentrovato, Helen Burke,
Susan Marra, Jennifer Scavo, Toni Warren, Sonja Willett

DEDICATION:

This collection of stories is dedicated to our past residents.
May they rest in peace and may their loved ones find solace
in their memories.

TABLE OF
contents

HOW TO USE THIS BOOK:

1 Complete the death questionnaire located in the 'Resources' section of this book before reading on.

2 Find a time and place free from any distractions. Make yourself comfortable, bring a blanket, a cup of tea, and a pen and paper, this time is for you and our story.

3 Read with curiosity, commitment, and a clear mind.

4 Once you reach part two, use the suggested journal questions following each story to reflect with intention and purpose.

5 Share what you've learned from these stories, in reflection, and your life experiences with your community.

PREFACE

Death and dying are often taboo subjects, pushed to the side, buried beneath the surface, and discussed in whispered hushed tones. Despite the inevitable fact that we are all human beings with fleeting time, we continue to uphold this system of secrecy and shamefulness. This secrecy spans all aspects of our lives and can inhibit the success of our valuable time on earth. What is the greatest part of life suffering from this secret social rule? Our long-term success and eventual end-of-life journey. We have unconsciously banded together to create a system that does not put our life success first, rather it puts a continuous priority on fixing the eventually unfixable. From poor education regarding healthcare choices and end-of-life care options to unfit models of care institutions, we continue to put our valuable time last. But we have shielded our eyes from these concerns only to be thrust into a traumatic whirlwind of events when we ourselves are faced with death and dying. We are left helpless, uneducated, and overwhelmed with the finances, insurance struggles, care burdens, care wishes, postmortem wishes, and of course the psychological impact.

Yes, death and dying are traumatic, disheartening, awful, and can come dramatically and unexpectedly, choosing us all differently; but what if we knew death was coming? What do we do when we have received a terminal diagnosis and are facing the end of life? We continue to shield ourselves, we put off important activities like creating a will, completing advanced directives, sharing with others, and even delaying the start of end-of-life care such as Hospice. We remain uneducated, do not ask for help, and maybe with the support of a physician continue to fight exhaustedly to delay what we know is once again, inevitable. This eventually turns into a discussion on how and where to live your final days. Because of our delicately composed world and its taboos of dying your options are few and far between. For medical support, you may approach and accept Hospice care or you may attempt to manage alone. For placement, although 7 in 10 individuals wish to die at home, you may be forced to face opposing models of care such as nursing homes, assisted living facilities, or hospitals.

These models of care exist for those who have no caregiver to be present each day, who have advanced care needs or lack adequate financial resources, but often fail to address these needs. So what happens if you lack financial resources, are unfit for a nursing home, but cannot remain uncared for in your own home or your caregivers are unable to continue care? Again, your options are few and far between.

Society has been searching for the answer to successful end-of-life care that promotes quality, compassion, and life fulfillment for hundreds of years. From the creation of hospitals, nursing homes, assisted facilities, to the development of models of care such as Hospice and Palliative Care, we continue to work toward change year after year. A substantial step toward change occurred with the development of residential care homes in Western New York. Advantages of these residential "comfort care" homes, later came to be known as "community comfort homes", "comfort homes for the dying", or "comfort care homes" include:

- Decreased financial burden, including zero cost or sliding scale payment

- A Home-like setting, provided by community members, to enhance the quality of life and care

- A continuum of care provided in conjunction with medical providers focused on addressing each individual's physical, emotional, and social needs

- Intimate and individualized attention and support for individuals and their loved ones

- Enhanced emotional and educational support provided in conjunction with medical providers for loved ones

- Connection and fulfillment are valued as a process of end-of-life and enhanced with community support

In 2006, a comfort home for the dying opened in Schenectady County, New York to address the needs of their community members. Their journey, stories, and testimonies are heart-touching and a powerful example of the future of end-of-life care and end-of-life perspectives.

WHAT IS HOSPICE?

Hospice is a medical provider that focuses on the quality of life for individuals and their caregivers who are experiencing an advanced, life-limiting illness. Hospice values compassionate care so that an individual may live as fully and comfortably as possible. Hospice care treats the person and symptoms of the disease, rather than treating the disease itself.

Who: Individuals with a terminal or severe illness and prognosis of 6 months or less

What: Medical care for symptom relief including comfort care, bedside care, and psychosocial care

How: Care is provided by a medical team including doctors, nurses, social workers, chaplains, home health aides, CNAs, community members, volunteers, friends, and family

Where: In almost any setting including a home, nursing home, assisted living facility, or inpatient hospital

Cost: Hospice care is covered under Medicare, Medicaid, most private insurance plans, HMOs, and other managed care organizations

Part I

Living with the Dying
THE JOURNEY OF A COMFORT HOME

INTRODUCTION:
By Helen Burke, Board Member

The dream of the Joan Nicole Prince Home arose from the concern witnessed by Hospice Nurses, Social Workers, and Pastoral Care staff in Schenectady regarding the fragility of care and support Hospice patients had available to them in their homes and community.

In response to this concern, a small group of community members banded together to find a solution. This group met regularly to brainstorm possible solutions and concluded that a community home was the clear answer to the problem at hand. How and where were the next problems at hand for the community team.

The how question was addressed by several significant contributions, including the cooperation of community corporations such as Amedore Builders and Curtis Lumber. Suddenly the dream quickly became a reality. Not far down the line, another big question arose, can a home providing 24-hour care, seven days a week with no source of reliable income survive? For success, this concept would require a small permanent staff, many trained volunteers, and a vast amount of support from the community. And for these past fifteen years, the dream has survived and flourished with community donations, volunteer support, and grants. A true blessing provided by an amazing and compassionate community.

During these years, the Home's two-fold mission to first offer Compassionate End of Life Care and second to offer End of Life Care Giving Training to its community members has brought enrichment and insight into the spirit of the Home and the care it provides. This spirit has enriched staff, volunteers, health science students, the memory for whom this home is named, the community at large, and all those that have blessed the home in life and in death.

It is this story, within these pages, that provides a glimpse into the unfolding of life at the Joan Nicole Prince Home.

A COMMUNITY HOME FOR THE DYING

The Joan Nicole Prince Home started as a passionate wish in the hearts of Hospice workers in Schenectady County, NY. In early 2000, the reality of end-of-life care scarcity and the lack of quality comfort care facilities and education became vastly apparent in Schenectady County, NY. Several Hospice cases represented financial insecurities, lack of caregivers, caregiver breakdown, and psychosocial issues making it difficult for the Hospice team members to place individuals at the end of life in living situations representative of their true needs. Essentially, there was not a place for these Hospice patients, with the fewest options and the most need, to go. One particular case outlined the journey to creating a comfort home in Schenectady County... A 38-year-old single mother of two school-age children was in Ellis Hospital. The woman suffered from metastatic breast cancer and her terminal symptoms required hospitalization for pain management. It became readily apparent that she could not be discharged back to her home to care for herself and her children with her disease rapidly progressing. There was not a family member who could temporarily provide care and relief, and the only nursing home bed available to her was over fifty miles away. After an exhaustive search of her options, she was transferred to that facility, and plans were set up for state guardianship of her two children. They relied on Hospice volunteers during the holiday season to transport them for infrequent visits to their dying mother. For the Hospice team, witnessing the young mother's end-of-life journey be filled with challenges, pain, fear, and insecurity, was heartwrenching in addition to her separation from her young children. With this mother's spirit at heart & the hope for better end-of-life journeys for future patients, the Hospice team swore to make a change.

In December of 2001, a former nurse of Community Hospice in Schenectady shared some inspiring news for the end-of-life care field. She shared her discovery of non-medical residences for the dying that were opening in Western New York with the working Hospice team. These homes relied on faith-based agencies for financial support and were partnering with Hospice home care programs to provide medical oversight. Patients who were screened and admitted to these two-bed residences had the fewest options for safe and comfortable home care in their own homes. Uniquely, unlike other hospice care facilities or nursing homes, these homes for the dying could become independent of state regulations, and room and board at these homes were not reimbursed by Medicare or Medicaid. With these unique characteristics, they frequently sought to become an arm of an umbrella agency to help with financial support, especially in the early development stages of their home. These homes stood out in a financial capacity but also in organizational operation, having only a few paid staff and relying largely on volunteers to provide hands-on care to the residents. But where to begin?

WHAT IS COMFORT HOME CARE?

Care available in a community home-like environment with a holistic approach that focuses on patient and family-centered care. Care is provided by community members and a few staff with the support of the local Hospice program. Caregivers act as surrogate family members and Hospice staff to provide 24/7 care.

Who: Individuals with a terminal diagnosis, a prognosis of 3 months or less, on Hospice care, has a Do Not Resuscitate Order, and is unable to live safely alone due to a caregiver breakdown or other outstanding need

What: Bedside comfort care for symptoms relief and management in addition to psychosocial care for patients and their loved ones

How: Care is provided by a mix of community members, volunteers, and health care staff 24/7 under a non-profit title, with the help of medical care (medications, changes in condition) provided by the local Hospice program

Cost: There is no cost to a patient or their loved ones to reside in a comfort home, however, there may be stipulations on length of stay, or a sliding scale payment option

Visiting the homes and reading their brochures was not enough. Thorough research and investigation was put in place to hastily move forward with the vision to develop a home in Schenectady County. Countless questions arose at the forefront of the Hospice team's minds... What do these homes look like? How are they funded? How are they run? What is the cost? How will it sustain? How will it help the community? Where would the home be located? What are the first steps?

In response, a steering committee of Hospice staff and community members was formed. To start they visited the comfort homes for the dying in upstate New York, now with the purpose of learning more about how they were developed, operated, and funded. The committee members visited the home in Saratoga and a home in Utica, both supported by Catholic Charities. These homes were two-bed residences. Additionally, the home in Rochester had a larger bed capacity and was supported by a local Hospice. These trips brought great inspiration and insight to the development needs of the future Schenectady County comfort home's steering committee.

By the start of 2002, the steering committee established to explore the feasibility of developing a two-bed residence in Schenectady County was strengthening in numbers and had a clearer outline of direction. With the onset of an opportunity from Hospice, the plan emerged. The Community Hospice Foundation was offering each of the regions it served a $25,000 grant to develop a two-bed residence if the following guidelines were met:

- Appoint a diverse board of directors of business people, lawyers, accountants, Hospice professionals, clergy, etc.
- Create the bylaws for the Board of Directors
- Create a mission statement for the Home
- Obtain a 501 (c) (3) status not-for-profit

These requirements were to be presented to the foundation in addition to a feasibility study, demonstrating the need of the community for such a residence. The steering committee shared the vision for the home, as well as the guidelines set forth by the foundation, in an open meeting of interested and committed community members recruited in the last few years. Soon following, the steering committee and Hospice team began to diligently keep track of inpatient and home care patients who would be better served in a non-medical comfort home under Hospice oversight and assembled the first board of directors of

Schenectady Community Home from a diverse group of professionals.

This board began to meet once a month to work on developing the Schenectady comfort home and completing the tasks set forth by the Foundations' call for proposals. Within one year the Schenectady Community Home became a 501(c)(3) with a strong mission statement: "The Schenectady Community Home is dedicated to providing a safe, comfortable, and caring residence for terminally ill individuals in need of a home in their final days."

While working towards the guidelines of potential funding from Community Hospice, the board created a subcommittee to seek further financial assistance for the development and long-term feasibility of the comfort home. The sub-committee was charged with visiting Catholic Charities in Schenectady and Albany to explore the feasibility of a financial operating partnership as many of the Western New York homes are funded as partnerships with faith communities. Although a partnership did not materialize, Catholic Charities did offer a diocesan property no longer used as a rectory for the cost of $25,000- the amount of the grant anticipated from the Community Hospice. After touring the facility the board was able to consult, in a pro-bono capacity, with a structural engineer who presented them with a detailed renovation design which converted the property to be handicapped accessible both inside and outside and replaced the heating and ventilation systems. Ultimately the board decided that renovations were too costly to undertake in addition, there was concern about safety and parking in the property's city location. This disappointment was short-lived, as a prominent business member on the committee began negotiations with a local builder to explore the possibility of building a new home in a local neighborhood of Scotia, where his company was building single-family homes. The reputable builder was enthusiastic about the project and giving back to the community. He agreed to build the home at cost, with promised donated services, and zero charges for upgrades once the funding had been secured. From there on out, 22 Glenview Drive in Scotia, New York was secured as the future site of Schenectady Community Home Inc.

An additional Board Committee worked with the builder to design the home according to the specifications required to serve terminally ill residents and families. While the plans were being made for a future home of the Schenectady Community Home, time was of the essence to secure financial support for a down payment. Fortunately, a banker on the Board worked to apply for a mortgage at the local bank where he was an executive. After countless hours, meetings, and commitment, the time came to meet with the Community Hospice and share the proposal for Schenectady Community Home Inc.'s comfort home. In addition to presenting the required guidelines, an additional model of care for serving residents and families in conjunction with the Hospice home care program oversight was presented. During the presentation, policies such as patient/family consent forms that the administration would require for a patient to be admitted to the Home and a screening process for eligibility for admission were discussed. The result of the meeting was in the favor of the soon-to-be comfort home, with one catch, the Community Hospice Foundation decided to only release the $25,000 grant if the board could raise $25,000 in matching funds. The board was faced with yet another challenge, to raise funds, but with the work already accomplished, they remained undeterred.

In the search for financial support, the board gave approval to one of the founding board members to approach a prominent real-estate businessman well known for his philanthropy for community not-for-profit projects. During the face-to-face meeting with him the history of the project, the mission statement, and the aspects of the development were thoroughly discussed. He offered excellent wisdom, advice, and validation of the work done to date. At the meeting's closure the man, who always insisted on remaining anonymous, pulled out his checkbook and wrote a check to the "community home for the dying" for $25,000. He stated emotionally that his only stipulation was that when the time came, each of the patient rooms be named after his two young sons who died tragically. The board, without question, agreed to place plaques outside of each patient room, one for Kyle and the other for Joshua. Very shortly after receiving $25,000 to match the Community Hospice's grant, he made contact with the board member stating that once the home was open he would provide $10,000 a year in restricted funds for food, beverage, and celebrations for the residents of the home.

After securing the donation from Hospice, the fundraising committee of the board earnestly worked to continue to find financial support for the project that had now become a reality. The committee focused on a public relations campaign to spread awareness of the project to the community at large and begin the recruitment of volunteers to be trained for resident care once the home opened. Additionally, the committee proposed three major fundraisers for the home, an annual capital campaign, gala, and 5K run/walk.

At this time, the board also set a new financial objective to pursue a legacy donation. Several individuals on the board were aware of a young 36-year-old mother of four who had died in the previous year of metastatic breast cancer. She was formerly a resident of Niskayuna who relocated to Virginia after she married to raise her family. Her husband, a graduate of Annapolis, was a wealthy businessman.

SECTION B MONDAY, FEBRUARY 14, 2005

SCHENECTADY
CITY & COUNTY
EDITION

LOCAL

THE DAILY GAZETTE

A WISH LIST drawn up by Scotia-Glenville School District officials will be discussed at a school board meeting to take place tonight. B2

THIS WEEK

Talk planned on restoration of fire tower

SCHENECTADY — The local chapter of Adirondack Mountain Club will host "Saving the Spruce Mountain Fire Tower," a program by Jack Freeman at 7:30 p.m. on Wednesday in the McChesney Room of the Schenectady Public Library, 99 Clinton St.

Freeman will speak about his efforts to restore the fire tower and gain permanent access to the hiking trail leading to it.

SCOTIA

Care home eyed for terminally ill

Fund-raising drive aims for $1 million

BY MARY MARTIALAY
Gazette Reporter

About a year and a half ago, Cheryl MacNeil arrived as a hospice volunteer at the door of an elderly man. She was expected, but when she rang the man's doorbell, there was no answer.

"So I called him on my cellphone. And I said 'Hi, I'm outside your house,'" MacNeil recalled. "And he said 'that's fine, but I'm bedridden.'"

After a few phone calls, MacNeil went to the management office of the apartment complex where the man lived, and was let into his house. There she found the man lying in his bed, as he had done most of the day.

"He had a son who worked and came at night, and there was a nurse's aide who came in at lunch . . . to take care of his hygiene," MacNeil said. "But the rest of the day, he sat and he lay in bed in a room with one window."

Recently, MacNeil became the executive director of Schenectady Community Home Inc., which was formed to aid terminally ill patients who wish to remain in a homelike setting, but do not have family or friends to care for them.

With the help of local builder Amedore Homes, the three-year-old group soon hopes to build a care home in the Stone Ridge housing development in Scotia with room for two terminally ill patients.

The group will launch a fund-raising campaign with a mailing next week, and hopes to raise $1 million to pay for the home and five years of service. The home will cost $254,000. The group expects to spend $120,000 per year on operating expenses.

MacNeil said the group wants to break ground by May and open in the fall of 2005. The group is also looking for volunteers to staff the home.

The idea for Schenectady Community Home has its roots in hospice care. But hospice care relies on family and friends to care for patients in between visits from professional staff. The patients who would live and die in Schenectady Community Home do not have that support, said MacNeil, who was hired in September.

"These are people who are alone. They don't have the family, or the family doesn't have the resources," MacNeil explained. "There's a lot of circumstances in this community where people have been for the better part of the day alone."

Organizers are careful to say that Schenectady Community Home is independent of Community Hospice of Schenectady, an organization that provides hospice care. The two groups are collaborating on the home.

Schenectady Community Home will raise its own funds to build and run the home and maintain its own volunteer roles. Community Hospice will provide the professional staff for end-of-life care at the residence. Three years ago Community Hospice also donated $25,000 in seed money for the organization.

MacNeil described the community home as a surrogate family

See HOME, page B2

![MacNeil]

Fundraising efforts were set forth to begin building the Home in 2005, with a tentative plan to open in the Fall of 2005.

BROOKDALE 2

2 Story, 3 or 4 Bedrooms, 3 Baths

1,516 sq. ft. - 1st floor
801 sq. ft. - 2nd floor
2,317 total square footage
Square footage and room sizes are approximate.

Amedore☆
H O M E S

Because several of her extended family members and friends lived here locally, her story, and especially her resilience and strong faith resonated with the board. In time, a board member who knew her husband approached him with a gesture of heartfelt condolence. She asked permission to send each one of his children bereavement bears, in which their mother's clothing would be repurposed to outfit the bears. In that same letter, the board member said these were gifts from the board of a not-for-profit organization and explained the history of the project and its mission. He graciously accepted the offer of the bereavement bears for his children. Several months later, the same board member re-approached the husband conveying to him that his late wife had many similar qualities to the young woman who had inspired the vision for the Schenectady Community Home Inc. A thorough update of the ongoing construction process as well as mortgage approval and fundraising campaigns were included in the request for consideration of a legacy donation and proposal to name the Home after his late wife. The board did not have to wait long for his affirmative response and notable donation. Henceforth the community Home for the dying (Schenectady Community Home Inc.) would be known as The Joan Nicole Prince Home (JNP Home).

Soon after receiving the amazing gift of a legacy donation, the Board of Directors and community supporters broke ground on August 1, 2005, with the builder in a quiet neighborhood on a corner lot in Scotia, New York. The local Daily Gazette press release revealed so many smiling and proud faces, as it had taken several years to arrive at that moment.

Early in the development of the home, the board had agreed to hire a grant consultant to explore grants that might be available for non-for-profit operating expenses, now that the reality of building was underway, grant writing would be expanded to include capital expenses. The building committee met with the builder to address the home's design with needs for handicapped-accessible bathrooms in each of the resident's first-floor rooms. A living room, kitchen, small visiting parlor, and laundry room with guest/staff bathroom were all to be included on the first floor where all resident and family activity would take place. The upstairs of the home would include an office for staff and a room for resident's family members who might require overnight accommodation. There would also be a bathroom with a shower between the two rooms for staff and family members who might need to occupy the upstairs bed.

While the home was being built, another committee was choosing the furnishings for the home. Each resident's room was equipped with an electric hospital bed, a barcalounger, an over-the-

On August 1st, 2005, Schenectady Community Home Inc. broke ground to begin construction.

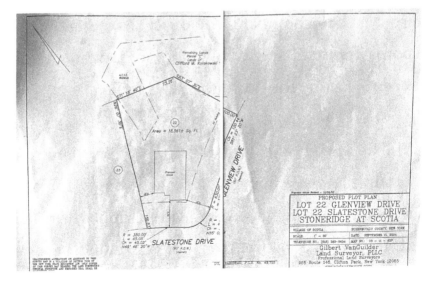

bed table, commode, dresser, closet, and bedside stand. Joan Nicole Prince's husband donated flat-screen TVs for each of the residents' rooms and DVD players were procured. Each resident's room included their own private bathroom with handicapped accessible toilets, showers, and sinks. Residents would be free to bring personal belongings to make their rooms more comfortable and feel at home. It was very important to Joan Nicole's local relatives that the furnishings in the home reflect her taste, both in colors and comfort. Local furniture businesses were extremely generous and very helpful, by providing discounts on purchases, just a small sample of the community contributions to come.

The kitchen table was donated by a local craftsman. The Schenectady Medical Auxiliary donated the funds to furnish the downstairs visiting parlor and a local pathologist provided money to furnish the upstairs family room. The Community Hospice staff volunteered funds for the outdoor furniture and the storage closet, turned meditation room, which was painted and decorated by Joan's local family members who informed us she came to one of them in a dream "and said please provide a small meditation room for the families to use!" The final touch to decorating was a beautiful portrait of Joan Nicole Prince, commissioned and paid for by one of her friends, which rests above the fireplace in the living room for all to see.

Throughout construction and designing, the home was made handicap accessible- including a ramp in the garage, wider doorways, and hallways. In the discussion of making the home accessible, the board decided that durable medical equipment such as wheelchairs, commodes, and walkers would be donated to the home using the patient's Hospice Medicare/Medicaid benefit. The Home would also accept basic patient supplies as donations such as adult attends, toiletries, mattress pads, wound care

Pictured Above (Left to Right): Joshua Room, Kyle Room, Front Sitting Room & Kitchen
Pictured Below: Main Living Room

Joan Nicole Prince's potrait and the Joshua and Kyle Room plaques remain in the Home till this day.

supplies, bedpans, personal care items, etc. to make sure each and every resident had needed supplies available to them at all times.

On the organizational side, the board's awareness campaign led to hiring its first Executive Director to help coordinate the building process and recruit patient volunteers. The director was assigned to work closely with the committee that was charged with setting up all of the practical and daily operations to provide 24-hour compassionate, safe, and competent care as well. Experienced Hospice and community professionals on the board worked tirelessly to write procedures, screening protocols, and consent forms consistent with the planned model of care. The Community Hospice staff was consulted regularly in this process as they were providing medical oversight to the residence. In planning, the JNP Home's model of care was solidified as a non-medical comfort home for Hospice patients who were referred to the Executive Director and two residential care coordinators for 24-hour care. These staff members would act as liaisons to Hospice as well as advocates and educational teachers for the non-profit. However, their main job was to provide the care as directed by the Hospice plan of care in conjunction with Hospice and community volunteers. The home's policies and procedures for patient care were formed to complement the home's model of care:

- The patient must be enrolled in Community Hospice Care
- The patient must have a current do not resuscitate status
- The patient and family must consent to care being delivered by a combination of male and female staff and volunteers
- The patient must consent to a three-month length of stay, and understand a plan will be made to review options for further care once the length of stay had been reached

- Have a likely prognosis of three months or less to live
- Consent to having all patient care decisions regarding medical support and discharge be made in conjunction with their Hospice team
- The patient cannot require extraordinary care needs or life-sustaining care methods such as IVs, dialysis, feeding tubes, etc.
- The patient has the fewest options and the most need for care
- Patients are not charged in any way or means for their stay including room/board, meals, bedside care, etc.

After years, soliciting, fundraising, designing, building, and more, the Home finally opened in June 2006 after the first volunteer training course was completed. Before welcoming the first resident on June 19th, 2006, an open house was attended by Hospice staff, JNP Staff, board volunteers, and caring community members to celebrate. Several of Joan's local family members were present, alongside her parents who traveled up from New Jersey for the celebration. A local clergyman offered a heartfelt blessing of gratitude. Joan Nicole Prince's mother sat in the meditation room greeting visitors and between laughter and tears, she said repeatedly "Joanie would be so proud!" In the summer Joanie's husband and his children visited the home as well and they were moved by the beautiful portrait of his late wife and mother of his children above the fireplace. A true sense of gratitude prevailed as staff, volunteers, residents, and their families were able to thank him for his generosity in helping the vision of a safe home for all, a reality.

Although the opening of the Home was a triumph in itself, there was still more work to be done. In the first operational years, there was great concentration on assessing the needs of the residents, families and friends, building community partnerships and establishing necessary policies, procedures, and guidelines. Policies and procedures regarding employee guidelines, initiation and evaluation of referral and screening procedures, post-care evaluations, daily operations, and volunteer training programs were just a few examples of the procedures established in the first years. Shortly after opening, volunteer training programs and robust educational programs were initiated, with inservices for volunteers and staff provided by professional members of the community on a monthly basis. These training programs bloomed into educational partnerships, internships, and community partnerships that continued to grow each year. Through diligent hard work, dedication, and growth, the Home's policies, procedures, and educational programs became recognized by the Hospice and Palliative Care Association of New York State as a role model for comfort homes and often recommended to others who were considering establishing their own comfort home.

With the mastery of the Home's daily operations and programs, the Staff and Board of Directors began to focus their efforts on grant writing, sustainability, and endowment. With the nature of the Home's funding resources, grant writing became an essential part of the Staff's duties, but in order to ensure successful grant writing new policies for the collection of data were implemented. These policies included measurable assessment and evaluation tools and later on, thanks to Union College's C.A.R.E. Program, the creation of databases to store collected data. Through continuous dedication and determination, several grants were written and secured to ensure the sustainability of the Home's daily operations and successful caregiving. With a grant writing plan and implementation practices secured, the shift to focusing on endowment began.

This shift brought an endowment campaign, including planned giving, and a mortgage payoff campaign. Through successful grant writing, endowment campaigns, community support, and fundraising the Joan Nicole Prince Home stands fifteen years later.

15 YEARS LATER

The JNP Home has continued to grow each year through the dedication and generosity of the community. Since welcoming its first resident in June 2006, several changes have been made to adjust to the ever-changing care needs of terminally ill individuals at the end of life. Improvements and updates have been to ensure quality care for not only the resident but their loved ones as well.

One of these improvements included an addition to the mission and values of the Home to include educating the community and future health care professionals on end-of-life care. Since the beginning of JNP, the Home provided in-depth end-of-life care training with the help of Hospice and JNP Staff to volunteers. A few years into the running of JNP, partnerships with local colleges and their health professional majors emerged to fulfill a need for end-of-life care training and education. The educational programs offer critical educational experiences to which students otherwise rarely have access and increases the competencies of future health care providers in working with culturally diverse under-served populations. The training programs include but are not limited to, discussions on psychosocial care for patients and loved ones at the end of life, basic bedside care practices, cultural ideologies at the end of life, perceptions on death and dying, safety precautions, and providing medications. The JNP Home collaborates with numerous prestigious Capital Region colleges including Union College, Albany Medical College, Albany College of Pharmacy & Health Sciences, Maria College, SUNY Empire State College, University of Albany, The College of St. Rose, and more to change end-of-life care one individual at a time.

The JNP Home is dedicated to providing this

education for residents' loved ones as well. This allows them to return to being family members who can experience a better end-of-life journey with their loved ones, rather than remaining overwhelmed and fatigued caregivers. The Home has changed families' experiences of end of life by providing core lessons on death and dying, including what it means to face the end-of-life with dignity, what compassionate care and proper symptom management looks like, how to manage psychosocial struggles at the end of life, and the stages/process of end of life. The Home's dedication to educating and guiding families through the end-of-life journey is to inspire a better experience, one that can bring comfort, compassion, understanding, peace, fulfillment, and enhance the close connection between family and resident.

THE ROLE OF THE CAREGIVER

According to the Family Caregiver Alliance (FCA), a family caregiver is an individual who provides a consistent spectrum of assistance to an individual diagnosed with a long-term illness. These caregivers have a significant personal relationship and may live with or separately from the person receiving care. These are a few of their daily tasks as a caregiver...

Personal Care:

- Assist with ambulating and/or turning and positing
- Assist with hygiene and bathing
- Assist with toileting
- Assist with dressing and appearance

Medical Care:

- Coordinate medical appointments
- Assist with attending appointments
- Organize and administer medications
- Monitor and manage symptoms and medication side effects
- Monitor and document progression and general health condition

Nutrition:

- Prepare all appropriate meals
- Serve meals and assist with feeding if needed
- Monitor and document food and drink intake

Housekeeping:

- General cleaning of the living spaces including bedroom, bathroom, living room, and kitchen
- Wash, dry, and put away laundry, wash and dry dishes, sweep and mop floors
- Maintenance of living spaces for safety

Daily Tasks:

- Monitor and manage finances
- Update and maintain advanced directives
- Hold and maintain a steady income
- Provide emotional support and positivity for your loved one
- Communicate with appropriate medical providers and other family members

To provide continuous support to resident's loved ones the Home offers remembrance services twice a year to remember those served at the Home and sends post-care evaluation surveys to ensure successful quality care, changing policies and procedures based on feedback as needed. The Home offers fundraising campaigns to celebrate the lives of those who have passed at the Home as well, including personalized Christmas ornaments, and engraved bricks.

In May of 2009, the JNP Home was fortunate to fulfill two dream projects of creating a beautiful garden and educational training center, which came true with the support of General Electric, their employee volunteers, and grants. Together the team created a garden pathway for personalized bricks and a gorgeous water fountain for the backyard. Years later, the pathway has become filled with memorial and honorarium bricks, the garden tended to by hundreds of volunteers, and loved by so many residents. The educational center was completed in the basement following the installation of an in-kind storage room and procurement of necessary training supplies such as tables, chairs, and a projector. The training room continues to be utilized throughout the year for individual training sessions, yearly

Pictured Above (Left to Right): Joshua Room, Kyle Room, Front Sitting Room & Kitchen

Pictured Below: Main Living Room

Pictured Above (Left to Right): Family Room, Kyle Room Bathroom,
Joshua Room Bathroom, Meditation/Prayer Room
Pictured Below: Main Living Room & Kitchen

training, in-kind donation storage, and board meetings.

Throughout the years, small community-led projects such as an outside picnic table and bench for residents and their loved ones were contributed from the local Boy and Eagle Scout Troops. Since the opening of the Home, troops, clubs, societies, rotaries, and community churches have tended to the garden, provided yard clean-up, house cleaning, office work, and the collection of in-kind donations in addition to volunteer and fundraising support. Research projects and data collection to guide successful grant writing has been spearheaded by Professor Carol Weisse, Ph.D. and Union College's C.A.R.E. (Community Action Research and Education) Program. The C.A.R.E. program not only provides future health care professionals with hands-on end-of-life care training but produces research that validates the powerful outcomes of comfort homes with evidence based science as well.

Renovations to enhance the Home's welcoming atmosphere began in 2020 after the community raised $1,500 via Social Media platforms. This renovation project rapidly progressed, with community support and generous gifts of volunteer support and grants from Habitat for Humanity of Schenectady County, Eastern Parkway United Methodist Church, Village Paint & Decorating, Best Tile, Bennett Contracting, Paul Perry Kitchens, Wood & More Store, Schenectady Rotary Club, and community members.

The Joan Nicole Prince Home remains blessed by the generosity and support of the local community and beyond. As a 501(c)(3) non-profit, the JNP Home continues to run solely on donations and grants to support its $250,000 annual budget; still a challenging feat years later. With the support of the local community, board members, staff, and volunteers the JNP Home holds several fundraising events throughout each year to raise funds for the mission and sustainability of the Home, including an annual gala, 5k run and 1-mile walk, letter campaign, and several community-supported events. The JNP Home remains a unique model of care and is open to residents from throughout New York State's Capital Region. The Schenectady Community Home has continued to responsibly and successfully operate to provide a high level of quality care, with fine-tuning and adjustments made to daily operations, policies, and procedures as deemed necessary.

Despite a closure due to the 2008 recession and tremulous times during a global pandemic, the JNP Home stands tall, is supported, and makes a difference for the Schenectady County community every day. There remains a steady waiting list for residency and a stream of new referrals for the two-bed capacity and countless new volunteer applications each year. To date, the JNP Home has served over 225 residents, their families, hundreds of future health care professionals, and community members. Countless volunteers, community members, and organizations have provided direct bedside care to residents, helped maintain the Home inside and out, and assisted with the growth of the Home from fundraising to outreach.

For fifteen years, the Joan Nicole Prince Home has been witness to hundreds of individuals' lives and their end-of-life journey. Their time spent with the volunteers and staff at the Home shed light on countless life stories, struggles, wishes, passions, family concerns, family growth, friendships, celebrations, and so much more.

Part II

Stories & Testimonies

Stories

From Joan Nicole Prince Home
Staff, Volunteers, and Family Members

A Hand to Hold

Often I am faced with a resident who is unable to verbally communicate when they are close to passing. It can be a difficult situation for families and volunteers and it poses the question, how do we connect with our loved ones when their verbal communication is taken away? And as I reflect on what I did in those moments, I realized when I let go of my concerns and worries about having perfect communication, my actions were instinctual. I would stroke their hair, talk to them about the weather or their family, read them a book, but the most prevalent action I would take was holding their hand. A simple gesture of holding someone's hand is often so intimate. We hold the hands of our partner to show affection, our child to show safety, but when we hold the hand of someone we recently met it could be strange. But I have generally found when I do hold a resident's hand, there is a change within them and within our connection. They visibly become more relaxed, their breathing slows down, their hand once cold now becomes warm, and the entire atmosphere fills with comfort and a warming connection. And this simple gesture to connect, which was providing meaning and relief for me, is now providing comfort, relief, and a sense of security for someone who is bravely continuing on their journey.

Journal Question:

What makes you feel safe? How do you wish to be comforted when sick or ill?

Just Right
──────🔆──────

We all have that one meal that is only perfect when a specific person makes it. They always seem to have the special ingredient, special cookware, or a secret to make it just right. For me, it's my grandma's pickles, I know no one else can make them the way she makes them. When I first met Frank, I quickly learned his "just right meal" was a simple sunny-side-up egg. He was the one who made it perfect, who added the right amount of salt and pepper, created the perfect seared bottom, and placed it perfectly on top of toast. But, Frank was no longer able to cook for himself and quickly missed his "just right meal". The second day he was at JNP before he woke and was wheeled to the kitchen table, I got out all the necessary items to make his "just right" sunny-side-up egg, or at least something close to it. When he made it to the table I had him supervise the cooking, he told me the instructions and I followed through as he watched from the table. Egg number one didn't make the cut, but I didn't give up hope! Egg number two was just a disappointment as Frank became frustrated that he would never taste his egg again. The next day, bright and early, I got to work on Frank's egg. As he sat at the kitchen table and I cooked, we talked about how he was feeling, in between his directions to keep the heat on low and when to add the salt and pepper. I placed the egg onto the lightly toasted piece of toast before serving it to Frank. As I started cleaning up, knowing the egg would not be perfect I was thinking of the tasks ahead that day, but to my amazement, my thoughts were interrupted by a "took you only three days to perfect it". I looked up at him and just smiled. He ate the entire meal that day and the rest of the day, he was very content.

※

Journal Question:

What is your legacy? What do you want to pass to others and be remembered for?

BROWN LEAVES & SNOWFLAKES

From your window, I watched the last brown leaves of fall being blown down, mingled with snowflakes. One season-ending, another beginning. Suddenly I realized that you might be between seasons as well. Your journey through this earthly life ending the promised life eternal beckoning. The house was filled with family and friends talking and laughing. Your husband never left your side. The two of you had a love for the ages. He had cared for you at home for months on end until he could no longer manage alone. You had been with us for three months. Your dying time was near but we knew you would fight right up until the end. Who would want to give up what you had? We kept you comfortable out of the request of your family and our mission, but it did not affect your process at all. As I stood at the foot of your bed your husband said "what now? You're the quarterback". Well, as they say when all else fails, look up, I said. So as the dry leaves and snowflakes fell my prayers went up. As I sat beside you gently stroking your forehead and speaking softly you slowly started to relax. Your labored breathing slowed until it was no more. While the wind chimes rang, the angels guided you through the changing seasons, through the brown leaves and snowflakes.

☀

Journal Question:

What would you want your final goodbye to your loved one to look like? Consider what you would wish to say, how would you want it to feel?

Surprise Blessings

A couple of months in a row, I have come into the Home to find fresh pastries, cookies, soups, and bread. When I asked where they came from I was told a woman came by and dropped them off. I pondered for a while who this person was, what is her name? How can I send her a thank you card? One day I finally got to meet her, she knocked on our door mid-morning with a delivery of soup & fresh bread, I introduced myself and told her thank you for all the times she had donated food for our residents and the volunteers. I then asked her name and asked if she wanted to come into the Home for a tour (she had never been inside). She refused to give me her name stating, "I just wanted to show my appreciation, I don't need a thank you, I don't want to be acknowledged." I reluctantly said okay after asking "are you sure?" eagerly several times. As the day went on and everyone enjoyed the fresh food, I was continuously replaying the interaction with the generous stranger in my mind. How wonderful it was that she took time and money out of her day to show her appreciation for our mission. Being in a residential neighborhood is a powerful aspect of our Home, as we are integrated beautifully into our community. Neighbors and community members will often stop by our Home to drop off surprise blessings of food, office supplies, cleaning supplies, and donations of patient supplies. We are grateful to have so many community members think of our Home and greet us with love and acceptance.

☀

Journal Question:

What do you love most about your community? Are there times you wish you were more involved in your community?

Acceptance

The first day I met James, was the first day he came to JNP. The first two hours of my shift passed quickly as I helped James' family store his items and get settled. Then James had lunch at the kitchen table, relaxed and at ease as if he had been there for years. After lunch I joined James in his room, to give him my undivided attention. "I've had a good life", he said. His tone was practiced as if repeating it had helped him to accept it. That is, no longer pursuing treatment for his cancer diagnosis. "I've had a good life." He was prepared. In the span of about forty-five minutes, he shared several remarkable and meaningful tales, as well as practical steps he had taken to get his affairs in order. I was captivated by his attitude! Residents like James are a gift to the volunteers and staff in the home.

Journal Question:

What does "a good life" mean to you?

Why Me?

I am often asked why I dedicate my time to the Joan Nicole Prince Home. Years ago, I attended an informational meeting at my church about this home and the need for volunteers. I signed up that very night. I figured, if I discovered it was not for me, I could always do something else to provide support. Well, fifteen years later I am still here. This is where my heart is, this is where I belong. The general thought is that it would be depressing to work around dying people all the time. But that is wrong, I work with living people. Living people who are ending their life's journey. They still have so much to offer, stories, lessons, memories, joy, laughter, and we in turn offer comfort, acceptance, and compassion. We offer the power of education, understanding, acceptance for our residents and their loved ones and this creates a space of light, hope, and peace to support times of sadness. Together we laugh and cry, rejoice, and mourn as one big family. This is not depressing, rather an acceptance and understanding of life's bountiful and ever-changing journey.

☀

Journal Question:

Is there something you have been drawn to or feel passionate about? If so, what actions have you taken to make it a part of your life?

Hidden Treasure

Wyatt was an older gentleman who came to us because of a CHF diagnosis. Always upbeat, great sense of humor, Wyatt loved chocolate chip cookies, more specifically, my chocolate chip cookies. Every time I came he would be out of my fresh baked cookies and ask for more. So I finally asked him how he could eat so many cookies by himself. With the big grin, he was so famous for, he pointed to the bottom drawer of his nightstand. There were containers of cookies, almost empty again. He told me that he hardly got any cookies at all because everyone else helped themselves. So to make sure he got some, he had started hiding them so they would last longer.

Wyatt out-lived his three-month stay at JNP and when it was time for him to leave, I presented him with a whole bag of chocolate chip cookies with his name on it. My final image of him was him clutching the bag, with a huge grin on his face as he left the Home.

☀

Journal Question:

What food or item would you request in your final days?

Mother Nature

When I first met Alice, I wasn't sure what to think...she was the most alive person I had ever met and she was terminally ill with a prognosis of three months. Everything from her personality to her clothes and decor showed who she was; a fun, joyful, adventurous individual. I helped her unpack her things and helped her set up her room when she came to JNP. It was the first time a resident had ever decorated their room with rocks, sticks, and leaves, but it was a beautiful sight to see. She told me where to put everything and as I placed each item, she told me why it meant so much to her. I remember leaving that day and hoping people understood her quirkiness, understood why her nature collection meant so much to her. Alice was often found outside collecting more sticks and rocks for her collection. As I came to learn over the course of the next three months, Alice's life had been often unkind and presented her with many challenges that still had an impact on her. It was only after getting to know her and her family more intimately that I truly realized why nature was so important to her. For Alice, nature was always there, it was the mother it says to be, it was a friend. And that is why nature and surrounding herself with it was so comforting for her. With nature by her side, she found peace, respect, honesty, happiness, and value. I am so grateful that Alice was able to bring her nature collection with her to JNP and that she continued to interact with nature until the day she passed. I am so proud that everyone at JNP accepted and loved Alice for who she was, together we made her nature, and together we were by her side sharing in that peace.

☀

Journal Question:

What brings you peace and comfort? Where do you feel

accepted and valued?

Somewhere Over the Rainbow

Dwayne had a brain tumor, and when he came to us it had progressed and created several symptoms, including changing his mood. He was my first resident as a student volunteer and it was only my second or third volunteer shift. As I looked at him in the bed and the faces of his family full of sadness, I was worried I wasn't able to help them or him. Who am I to offer help? I am just a student. I grew worried these painful memories of his anger and sadness would overpower their past memories with him. One day we heard a family member trying to help him get repositioned (it wasn't going well), he was getting mad, agitated, verbal; so we stepped in. I saw the sadness in the family members' eyes. My volunteer mentor sat them down and then we talked to our resident. She made it funny and uplifting- how could she be light-hearted right now? How does she know this isn't who he truly is? Even though her knowledge of him was only based on family members sharing memories, she knew there was more to him than his symptoms. He continued to get frustrated and the time came for a distraction. The volunteer began to sing. It was at that moment I had to do something I didn't expect to do. I had to give my voice, something that has always been with me, but often felt pushed. At that moment I sang "Somewhere Over the Rainbow" and to our surprise, he became calm. I still see his family from time to time, and each time they tell me they have it recorded and often listen to it to remember their father is at peace.

☆

Journal Question:

Consider how you wish to be treated at the end of life... What measures do you want to be put in place to keep you comfortable? Whom would you want to be by your side?

Moments to Remember

Chris was a fascinating man. When I first met him at his home there was so much joy and pride in his eyes when he showed us all his belongings and shared with us his hobbies and memories. Chris loved his stuff, he had it everywhere, in several houses, a car he owned, in friends' houses, and with him at JNP. And he was very protective of these things. At the time, he was detached from many of his family members and friends due to his illness and its symptoms, so the volunteers and staff at JNP became his family and friends.

In the months to come, I had several conversations with Chris about his life, his decisions, and his illness; I came to truly know him.

One day as we sat outside, him smoking his cigarettes, me brushing birdseed off the porch, we started talking about his belongings. He was overwhelmed and anxiety-ridden by what was going to happen to his things. I asked him "What do you want to happen to your stuff?" He went into a long laundry list of what he wanted to go where, and whom he wanted it to go to. At the end of his winded statement, I asked him again, "What do you want to happen to your stuff?" He looked at me and said he wanted his things to be valued and remembered, he wanted people to remember his passion for his collections, he wanted to be remembered.

As days went by with Chris (and getting him a lawyer to help with his affairs) we talked here and there some more about his belongings. Then, one day as we sat at the kitchen table playing Canasta with a student volunteer and he shared with us the (made up) rules, we had the time of our lives. As the game ended, the volunteer said "Well Chris, every time I hear about Canasta or play cards I am certainly going to remember you." I knew that meant a lot to him.

☀

Journal Question:

Have you completed Advanced Directives to document your

desires at the end of life? Do you have a Living Will?

The Choice

When we welcomed Janet to JNP, we were all very surprised that she had an advanced brain tumor and was given a prognosis of three months or less; she was still extremely active and was able to take care of herself. She was walking around without assistance, cooking her meals, and crafting. The only thing that would indicate a terminal disease was her occasional pain and slight confusion. Our student volunteers loved learning from her and were often found spending time together outside or crafting and listening to music at the kitchen table. Despite the positive time she was having at JNP, Janet was struggling with her diagnosis. She often confessed to me that she didn't feel sick, wanted to do things on her bucket list and that she wasn't ready to die. Over the course of two months, we had several conversations regarding these confessions. They often focused on what her illness was, how it progresses, and what her friends and family wanted her to do.

One day I found her in the garden very upset, she said she wasn't sure she wanted to be on end-of-life care anymore. She told me that seeing and meeting all the wonderful volunteers has brought her and helped her to discover her true desires. But there was a catch; she was fearful about what others would say or think, all of her family and friends wanted her to receive end-of-life care services and slow down. As we watched the fountain flowing and the birds flying around, we talked about all the things we had discussed since her arrival. Very casually, as if we had been friends for thirty years, I asked "what do you want to do?" she looked at me and said, "I want to fight, there is more I want to do." I encouraged her to remember that we all have the right to make choices for ourselves, even if we are sick or ill.

Janet left JNP and signed off of end-of-life care

services the next day. She left with a smile on her face and lived for several months afterwards.

Journal Question:

How will you stand up for your medical desires?

Light in the Darkness

When I was a student volunteer, we had a resident with a very large and caring family. Often the morning was quiet, he would sleep until the afternoon, wake up to some fresh coffee, from his special percolator, and then his family would visit until after dinner time. It was such a wonderful sight to see the family come together and have so much love in the Home. Though they knew their loved one was very sick, there was rarely a moment of complete sadness. In fact, there was often acceptance and understanding of what was to come. I always admired their courage and state of mind, as I was unaware of how I might handle this situation if it was my family member. On a beautiful afternoon, his family came with his three-month-old granddaughter. We all watched as his eyes lit up holding her and smiling. Everyone took pictures, talked about her birth, and shared so many laughs. As the day came to a close and it was time for me to leave, I noticed my soul was filled with such lightness and hope. Our resident and his family had shown me the light in the darkness; the parallels of life and death were not so different, after all, they are both filled with gratitude and love.

$$\downarrow\!\!\downarrow$$

Journal Question:

What brings you gratitude? Write down five things that you are grateful for.

Safe Haven

My first resident as a staff member was with us for three months. We had grown extremely close to her and her family, we knew their story and history and we were all connected because of this. When she started to transition and was actively dying, it was difficult for the family and all who had come to know her. She fought for a long time and was refusing to "let go". So we tried every trick in the book to help her move on. Her children went in individually and said their goodbyes, her family together and separately told her it was okay to go, we let her be alone with relaxing music, but she was still fighting. Two days later, her husband sat at the foot of her bed, her children talking in the living room, and a staff member gently stroking her hair, she passed peacefully at midnight. The room was filled with tears. But eventually, her family was in her room, seated around her bed and from the kitchen, all we could hear was the sharing of stories and laughter. Once the funeral home had come, the family decided to have some breakfast after the long night. They sat around the kitchen table as the sun slowly woke up and the dew settled on the lawn. I will never be able to explain the feeling I had as we sat laughing and sharing together. Looking back, I remember how grateful I am to have known them, to have been welcomed into their hearts and journey, and that they were at JNP. To this day, when I walk into the Home, I can still feel the beauty of this moment in the air.

Journal Question:

Describe your wishes for end of life. Do you wish to have a service or celebration of your life?

Precious Memories

When we welcome a new resident, we have the resident and their family complete a "get to know you" form. It asks for information like favorite food, music, TV shows, places traveled, occupation, family, etc. We ask for this information to better connect with our residents. As we always say... we get to intimately know our residents, from the food they love to how many pillows and blankets they need to be comfortable. In addition to our handy form, we encourage residents to bring items from home to make their room their own. We've had residents bring everything under the sun like pictures, stuffed animals, lamps, furniture, art supplies, and more! I love seeing a resident in their room at JNP when it's filled with things they love and moments from their life; we have learned so much about our residents from these precious items. One of the most meaningful items I have come across is a resident's blanket with all of their family members' photos on it. Not only was it a conversation piece, it also brought such joy to our resident to be wrapped up tight with it like she always had them there to hug. I know it brought her comfort and ease in her final days.

☀

Journal Question:

If you had to leave your home during your end-of-life journey,

what would you bring with you to your new home?

Back Porch Stories

There is a comfortable seating area, located on the back covered porch, overlooking the trees, flowers, and garden fountain at JNP. I have a fond memory of a resident who would spot hummingbirds over and over again. He mentioned that some volunteers never saw them, so he advised them to take the time to sit and wait for them.

At JNP, the residents decide where they would like to spend their time. Some enjoy being in nature so much that most of their day is spent on the porch. Meals are eaten here, hobbies are enjoyed, and many conversations flow naturally in this relaxed space. I have always believed in the power of nature and appreciated the Homes ability to capture nature's tranquility amid a suburban setting- I've sensed that those close to death have a better understanding of the natural world and can teach us a lot about how to enjoy it and each other.

Journal Question:

What brings you tranquility?

Friendship

Residents, Beth and Harriett, did not know each other before coming to the Home and it didn't take them long to become fast friends. They would have their coffee together at the kitchen table each morning and share the daily devotional. They would socialize a bit and convene together on what they would like for dinner and the Home worked to fulfill their request, even when they were "out of the norm" type of meals.

One day, I was with Beth as she was waking up from her afternoon nap when she asked if Helen was up yet. Harriett overheard the question and called from her room, "I heard that ... I'll be right there." They had a card game planned and were looking forward to the game and to being together. The two developed a comfortable relationship which they shared during the rest of their days. The image of them playing cards and conspiring at the kitchen table will always stay in my mind, these moments were meant to be shared in this time and this place.

☀

Journal Question:

How do you share life with others?

Full of Life

One time, we welcomed a woman who had been living alone at home and was weak and sickly upon entering JNP. After a few weeks at the Home, her color and overall well-being improved. Fran even sent a family member for her hairbrush and lipstick from her home, a drastic change from our first meeting!

Her stay was quite memorable as she was at the Home along with a 100-year-old man who insisted we call him "grandpa". Grandpa was quite spry and spent much time at the kitchen table conversing with Fran. They laughed and laughed as they reminisced about the old days when there were dance clubs, big bands, etc., and joked about the two of them "dancing on that kitchen table". Grandpa entertained us by singing old songs, one of which was recorded and posted on the JNP social media page.

It was quite a lively home during their stay, with so many wonderful gifts. Grandpa had belonged to his church choir and was well-loved by his fellow choir members. At Christmas time, they came and surrounded him, serenading him with church hymns and Christmas carols. It was a touching scene and was what the Home is all about, life and love.

☼

Journal Question:

What moments in your life will always stay with you?

Garden Wedding

Shay was a young woman in her late thirties when she came to JNP. She had a tough life, her family in disarray, but one of her dreams was to marry her long-time boyfriend, Ted. Well, you don't tell people who work with the dying a wish or dream without them making it come true. A huge circle of activity from board members, staff, and volunteers collectively pulled together all the makings of a traditional and beautiful garden wedding. The community was asked to support the effort and followed through with donations such as a wedding gown, tuxedo, flowers, cake, food, music, canopy, and memorable gifts to mark the day. It all came together to make this dream of Shay's come true.

Journal Question:

Have you had a wish or dream come true? If so, how did it make you feel?

The Bird Feeder

There is a bird feeder located outside in the front of each resident room at JNP. The bird feeder attached to the ramp is encircled with wire to discourage the squirrels and chipmunks, to no avail. I have many fond memories of our residents enjoying the birds, but the other critters as well. One resident, in particular, would squeal with delight as she yelled for me to come to look when she saw her friends at the feeder or perched on the railing. The birdfeeder illustrates that sometimes what frustrates us, such as the freeloading animals at the feeder, brings such entertainment, smiles, and laughs to our residents.

At JNP volunteers and staff understand what makes for a good life at the Home. No matter that the birdseed gets eaten by more than birds, if the residents are happy, that's all that matters! These memories help me remember to see that something we believe to be negative can be something positive if we view it through the eyes of our loved ones.

☀

Journal Question:

Write down three little things that bring you positivity or happiness.

Lights Out
———※———

I swear Liza came to JNP straight from Woodstock... She had the long frizzy hair, fringed belts, funky skirts, and bell-bottom jeans. Liza had Huntington's Chorea, a genetic disease of the central nervous system. This is marked by a movement disorder, behavior changes, and loss of cognitive function. This disease can be extremely painful, but that never stopped Liza from living her life. There was never a dull moment when Liza was here. A smoker, Liza was often worried that she would run out of cigarettes. And with Christmas just around the corner, she would miss seeing the Christmas lights and decorations. I knew of a smoke shop on a street with several little shops and restaurants which were beautifully adorned for the holidays so we loaded Liza and her walker in the car and off we went. We got to the smoke shop and took care of business there, then headed to the local store where she tried to use up all the money she had stored up on her benefits card. Thankfully, there was a very nice man who helped get the groceries to the car. On the way back to the Home, we took the scenic route, but Liza was very quiet. I glanced over her way and sure enough, she was sound asleep. Liza, later on, expressed how good it felt to go to the store and see the Christmas lights, and I am grateful I could take her.

☀

Journal Question:

What does your perfect day look like?

Connections

I had a special connection with a resident at the Home named Ginny. After welcoming Ginny into JNP I asked her where she was from and she replied, "a small town you probably never heard of." I soon learned she was from Hoosick Falls, my hometown as well. After several weeks of conversations, we discovered she graduated with my mom. While they were not close friends, we had a connection, our six degrees of separation. Listening to residents' stories allows you to share in their lives. They are alone and vulnerable in those hours, a time that they let us share with them. It is then we become their family too.

Journal Question:

What connects you to others? Write down three things that make you feel connected to those around you.

Pink Earrings

Julia was a tremendously funny and uplifting individual. Her time spent with us at the Home was full of laughter and joy. During my shift, if time allowed, I would sit with Julia at her bedside and we would talk and giggle for hours! Julia loved people and they loved her, everything she did was with a smile on her face.

My sister, who owns a jewelry business, had made breast cancer awareness earrings and necklaces, that were pink and gorgeous. Thinking of Julia and her fight with cancer, I gave them to her along with a pink hat with flowers on it that I had made. She completely lit up when I gave her these gifts and I felt so much joy to be connected with her in her time of need. The relationships we get to form with the residents at JNP is beautiful, authentic, and truly life-changing. Julia was buried in those earrings, necklace, and hat and that means so much to me. But what truly means the world, was her bright smiling face when I gave them to her.

☀

Journal Question:

Has someone changed your life for the better? How did they impact your happiness and the way you felt?

Living for the Moment
❀

As a resident, Erica brought in a picture of herself for her room. The picture showed her at Columbia University, where she attended school, playing in the snow. The smile on her face showed it all, it showed her love and enjoyment of life. This picture was a small glimpse of her life as she lived it; taking pleasure in the moment and always in touch with her inner child. Over her lifetime, she experienced loss and encountered obstacles, however, her life was so full and beautiful. Her life was full of adventures until her cancer took over. Many people have a bucket list of things they would like to do, but Erica lived her list. Every story told by her daughter and many friends who came to visit made her smile, sometimes you could even sense a bit of mischief as she reminisced.

I will always admire Erica for being so accepting in her mortality, she wasn't with the home for very long, yet in the short time, I witnessed her living her last days much like she lived her life; surrounded by wonderful people. Perhaps if more people looked at end of life through the lens of living while you are dying, there would be less fear of being uncomfortable or not knowing what to say. At the Joan Nicole Prince Home, we work towards this perspective because we know at the end of life, it's okay to cry, to be afraid, and not know what to say.

☼

Journal Question:
Do you have a bucket list? Create a list of things that you want to experience in your life and a list of things you have accomplished.

Little Oysters

Howard was a 77-year-old gentleman with cancer, who came to the Joan Nicole Prince Home for end-of-life care. Despite having a leg amputation at the hip, he was quite adept at using his trapeze apparatus and caring for himself. However, as time went on, he was no longer able to get around. One day we learned that his daughter, who visited almost every day, had a birthday coming up. And Howard was feeling bad because he had no gift for her. Maybe fathers don't realize how much they've already given...

So, as if by magic, the JNP staff presented a blue velvet box holding a beautiful pair of pearl earrings complete with a gift bag and all the trimmings to Howard for his daughter. He needed a little help signing the birthday card, which I'm sure is kept safely in a drawer until this day. Smiles and tears were abundant when he gave the present to his daughter. I will never forget how such a small gesture created such a beautiful moment for father and daughter.

☀

Journal Question:

What final gift would you hope to offer to a loved one?

Taffy

Taffy is a King Charles Cavalier therapy dog. He is a beautiful shade of brown, low to the ground, slightly large, has big beautiful brown eyes, loves cheerios, and always has one eye on his owner, John. John and Taffy come to JNP every week to visit each resident, the volunteers, and the staff. Smiles just appear when Taffy walks through the door. He makes quite a difference in what can be an ordinary, boring day. He makes no demands but does enjoy a pet or gentle scratch.

The calming effect he has on the residents and volunteers is a sight to behold. And while Taffy enjoys a belly rub, John engages in conversation and never seems to be in a hurry to leave. Together they are a therapy team as opposed to a dog and owner. Their effect seems to linger throughout the rest of the day. When they are around, worries and stress take a back seat to welcome bigger and brighter smiles. All because of one little dog named Taffy and his companion, John.

☀

Journal Question:

In times of darkness, who brings joy to your life? How can you replicate this joy for others?

The Goodbyes

Before school ended a student stopped by to let our 100-year-old resident know she was done with exams and heading home for the summer, a final goodbye. They shook hands and smiled at each other as she said goodbye. It can be uncomfortable for many to meet someone for the first time and quickly establish a relationship. This can be even more difficult if the new person is dying and you would soon be saying goodbye. There are questions running through your mind, what do you talk about? How do you act? What about all the what-ifs? Having conversations or visiting someone at the Joan Nicole Prince Home doesn't have to be overwhelming or different from typical interactions. This wonderful man had a lifetime of stories to tell, 100 years worth. Imagine hearing about his career, all those "good old days" stories, and looking through black and white photos and books! During the weeks Jack was at the Home, volunteers fell in love with him and his family. Jack was a kind and loving person, visiting him was like visiting with your grandpa, and we made him feel like he was our grandpa. Staff and volunteers become family to those who come to the home; they can become someones' mother, father, sister, brother, aunt, uncle, grandparent, something incredibly special especially when some individuals have no one. This touching moment of a student saying goodbye shows that the more time you spend with someone, the more you learn, and the more comfortable everyone becomes. At the Home, that means you begin to notice things like the wrong blanket on a resident's bed, their favorite movie, songs, foods, or what comfort measures work best. For some, having a terminal illness with limited life expectancy means they are doomed to being alone, due to others' fears and uncomfortable feelings about being with the dying. The fact is, that all individuals who are dying are still human individuals, still the same person as before. During this time in life, the Home encourages focusing on life and living, even though we all know the inevitable and difficult part of saying goodbye for the last time will come soon.

☀

Journal Question:

Describe a time you have had to say goodbye. How did it feel?

Do you wish it had gone differently?

Testimonies
❋

From Joan Nicole Prince Home
Volunteers, and Family Members

☀

" The care my mom received at the Joan Nicole Prince Home was unprecedented. At the time, I was working multiple jobs- barely making ends meet, not meeting the needs to take care of my own mother. There was no time for "free time", nothing fun that you would like to do with the person you will lose very soon. The Joan Nicole Prince Home took a weight off my shoulders that was just-there are no words...I could not enjoy my time with her before. When she moved into the JNP Home, it gave us an opportunity to spend time with her, just a pure time with her, not having to worry so much about the care that we have to do. I feel like we were able to get a lot of resolution by spending time with her. They loved her purely- when we saw her it was stress-less; it was what we wanted it to be. Every moment was priceless. "

☀

" My favorite things at the Joan Nicole Prince

Home is (1)A sense of community, whether with those who work in the Home, the other volunteers, or family members of the resident; everyone has a common goal and is willing to pitch in. It is a really nice environment to be a part of. (2)Hearing all the life stories and accomplishments from our residents, they all have done such amazing things in their lifetime and it is really nice to hear their story. (3)There is a really nice feeling you get when you know you are making a difference for one of the residents. Whether it is making them just a little more comfortable or putting a smile on their face, it is a great feeling. "

_\!/_

" I needed knowledge and to be able to take care of older people and dying people. I learn and love every minute I am at JNP. I learned from every single resident. I learned to just be there, sit, and give them what they need. It has developed my confidence and I was able to take care of my dad in my home, until his beautiful death. I learn every time I come. You do not know what you will find when you walk into the beautiful Home- you just give and surrender. It is a beautiful thing. I also cared for my mom and I was able to step up again and take care of her in my home, and it was beautiful. So, I thank these two beautiful deaths to the Joan Nicole Prince Home, for helping me be able to do a beautiful thing for my parents and to see them through to the end of their life. All the knowledge I needed was provided to me at this beautiful Home."

☀

" These days medicine is modernized to fix people, extend their life, let's see what the issue is and fix it as quickly as we can and as fast as we can; try to hide the idea of failure or that medicine doesn't have the answer to every single issue. I learned a lot from learning about the phases of the dying process. There truly was no comparison to what I learned from the residents I sat next to day in and day out. They were the teachers. I learned more from them than I ever could in a classroom setting. I got to witness these moments that make you step back and really reevaluate how someone's process of death really changes throughout. "

꧁

" Volunteering has offered me the strongest glimpse yet of why medicine matters to me and the profound impact it has had on my own learning and maturing. In medical and undergraduate school, we focus on diseases and their complexities. However, I now know that it's equally important to connect with people and see their lives through their perspectives and their experience in the dying process. I was able to see disease in its multiple manifestations and learned how healthcare providers are able to align patients' end-of-life desires with medical and palliative care to avoid physical, mental, emotional, and spiritual suffering. "

☀

" I learned that the most important tool to focus on throughout disease and the end-of-life process is the relationships we build and how to listen to each other. While death is eventual for everyone, medicine aims to prevent it as long as possible. Volunteering has shown me that we do not know how to properly die in our medical system and that in the final leg of our life's journey we ought to rejoice in the life we have lived, rather than the one we hoped to. "

☀

" He wanted everyone to know how much he appreciated all of you, what you did for him, not only to take care of his physical needs but also the enjoyment he got from conversations with staff and the volunteers. There were many wonderful 'intangibles" as well as the wonderful, attentive care. "

☀

" I can't begin to thank you for all you have done for my father and me. I'm sure you have heard it all before, so I'll try to tell you something maybe you haven't heard. Not only did you help my father die, but you helped him live. He was reborn the day he entered JNP, touched by the kindness of everyone involved in the JNP Home. He told me many times that never in his life had he been treated with such compassion. It moved him, freed him, and gave him a faith that he didn't always have. It gave him the strength to leave his pain behind and move forward. Thank you seems trivial, so I'll pass on that and tell you that I am changed for having known JNP. I am a better person for having had JNP in my life for three months. I will pay it forward...many times. "

☀

" In my sophomore year, I decided to start volunteering at the Joan Nicole Prince Home. I expected that working with people who were dying would be depressing. Nonetheless, I hoped the experience would help me gain insight into the medical field and my future career path. My time at the Joan Nicole Prince Home has changed me-both personally and professionally. As I sat in the room watching one of my patients die, I realized how fleeting time really is. I now understand that I sometimes have to go outside my comfort level in order to truly grow as a person, and growing is exactly what I did. "

⚜

" It has been incredibly touching to look back over the years and see the amazing dedication and commitment that many families and friends of residents served, how they continue to support the JNP home to this day, some since 2007. It is with heartfelt fondness that I reflect on the staff, subcontractors, and volunteers who still provide ongoing support.

I am truly grateful for the loving kindness, support, dedication, and life lessons learned during my time at the JNP Home. The blessings bestowed upon me are too numerous to mention, as I reflect on many days of tears, laughter, and joy. Thank you JNP Home for being there since 2006 and I pray you will be available to serve so many more in need for years to come! "

⚜

" I remember pulling up to the Home and thinking to myself, "what type of place is this, is this someone's home? I was expecting it to be a facility like a nursing home. I took a tour of the home and was immediately interested. Everything was so clean, decorated, and kept together, inside and out. I remember thinking, "this place is better than my house." I learned so much that first day, especially about the people that live at the Home. During my first shift alone, I talked to the resident about her life and family. I remember her specifically saying "most of my family is out of state and can't visit." I replied that we will be here and take care of her.

After caring for three residents, I noticed a recurring theme. I felt it was my obligation to be with these people when they are alone and dying. Three years of volunteering quickly passed and I joined the educational program with Union, in my research, I found about 11% of the past residents at the home had no caregiver, whatsoever. It's hard to imagine what they would have done if this Home didn't exist. I now realize how important the Home and other homes are, as well as how few exist.

I am thankful for all I have learned from the residents, staff, and other volunteers. Volunteering at the Home has definitely made me a better person and a better physician later in life. "

※

" Volunteering at the Home has not only made me more comfortable in dealing with death, which is a very difficult subject, but it has also helped me to better understand the importance of working with a team. "

※

" Our beloved Mom was fortunate and blessed to have been a resident at JNP. At 82 years young she was still working as a Home Health Aide when given the grim diagnosis of an inoperable brain tumor. From the moment we arrived, we were told to make ourselves at home. However feeling a little shy, we spent the afternoon turning down several offers of food and beverage. We watched as the other resident's granddaughter was bopping around the kitchen in and out of the refrigerator and microwave, but yet we still had that sense we were in someone else's home. That ended that day.

By day two we were the ones bopping around the Home and making ourselves at home. We were met daily by the most beautiful volunteers in the world, whether it was the adult volunteers, the college students, or the staff, they all gave us the impression there was no place in the world that they would rather be. They never failed to end every shift with a heartfelt hug, always wanting to ensure that our needs were being met as well.

Leaving Mom that first evening and every subsequent evening that followed, my family was given a gift. The gift of knowing she would be loved and cared for in our absence. Yes, there were many tears shed during those rides down Bancker Avenue, but that gift was nothing short of a miracle. I believe it was the Executive Director who said another resident once asked her "do you know why there are so many miserable people in the world?", she questioned, "no why?" The resident said, "because all the wonderful people are here!" From firsthand experience, truer words have never been spoken.

Sadly, our time at the Home came to an end on Day fifteen when our wonderful, loving mom ended her 45-day battle and joined our Dad.

However, the Home will forever be a part of our hearts and now our future. I'm reminded of a quote by Oliver Wendell Holmes Sr.- " Where we love is home, a home that our feet may leave, but never our hearts." Thank you to the entire staff for making such a difficult job seem simple and effortless. Especially for alleviating our fears and many times over saying, "you just need to be the daughter, we'll take care of everything else!" They are tireless heroes in our eyes and we will adore

them forever. "

❖

" There are not enough words in the English

language to express our thanks, to all of you, for

the loving care you gave Mom during her stay. Not

only did you care for Mom, but me as well. I am

truly humbled. All of you have a special place in

my heart. You are truly "angels" on Earth. God

bless each and every one of you. "

❖

" We would like to express our appreciation for the

care given to our Mother during her brief stay at

the Joan Nicole Prince Home. The entire staff and

volunteers showed great compassion and a true

sense of caring. You made my mother's last days as

comfortable and home-like as possible. I'm certain

that my mother found peace and comfort in this

environment. Everyone's commitment and

dedication to making her stay pleasant and pain-free was greatly appreciated. We learned a great deal about preparing for her passing from everyone. "

Resources

Death Questionnaire
―――✦―――

Adapted from R.A. Kalish & D.K. Reynolds, Perspective of Death and Dying, Vol.4 of Death & Ethnicity: A Psychocultural Study, 2nd Ed. (pp.200-221), 1981, New York: Baywood.

1　How many people whom you knew personally have died in the past two years?

　　None　　　　*1-3*　　　　*4-7*　　　　*8+*

2　How many of those people died as a result of _____?

Chronic Illness:	*None*	*1-3*	*4-7*	*8+*
Sudden Illness:	*None*	*1-3*	*4-7*	*8+*
Accident:	*None*	*1-3*	*4-7*	*8+*
Suicide:	*None*	*1-3*	*4-7*	*8+*
Homicide:	*None*	*1-3*	*4-7*	*8+*
War:	*None*	*1-3*	*4-7*	*8+*
Other:	*None*	*1-3*	*4-7*	*8+*

3　How many funerals have you attended in the past two years?

　　None　　　　*1-3*　　　　*4-7*　　　　*8+*

4 How often have you visited someone's grave, other than during a burial service, during the past two years?

   None　　　　*1-3*　　　　*4-7*　　　　*8+*

5 How often do you think about your own death?

   Never　　*Hardly Ever*　　*Monthly*　　*Weekly*　　*Daily*

6 Have you ever felt that you were close to dying?

   No　　　　*Yes*

7 Have you taken out life insurance for yourself?

   No　　　　*Yes*

8 Have you made arrangements for your body or organs after your death?

   No　　　　*Yes*

9 Which seems more tragic, a sudden death or a slow death?

   Sudden　　*Slow*　　*Equal*　　*Depends*

10 Which two deaths seem to be the most tragic?

   Infant Child Young Middle -Aged Elderly Depends

11 Which two deaths seem the least tragic?

   Infant Child Young Middle -Aged Elderly Depends

12 Which kind of death seems most tragic?

Natural   Chronic   Accident   Suicide   War   Depends

13 Have you taken out a will, arranged for someone to handle your affairs, or decided on your end-of-life wishes?

No   Yes

14 Do you want funeral/memorial services?

No   Yes

15 Do you want a religious funeral/memorial service?

No   Yes

16 Would you object to having an autopsy performed?

No   Yes

17 Where would you want to die?

Home   Hospital   Nursing Home   Work   Depends

18 What disposition would you choose for your body?

Burial   Cremation   Donation   Other

19 Where would you choose to have your funeral held?

Home   Religious Place   Funeral Home   Other

20 Regarding viewing of your body, casket open/closed?

Open   Closed   Depends

21 How many people who were dying have you visited or talked with during the past two years?

None　　　　*1-3*　　　　*4-7*　　　　*8+*

22 Have you witnessed someone die?

No　　　　*Yes*

23 Have you touched a dead body?

No　　　　*Yes*

24 If you were dying, would you want to be aware of your condition?

No　　　　*Yes*

25 With only six months to live, how would you spend the time?

Withdraw into yourself	*Living in the present*	*Focusing on others*
Arranging your affairs	*Denying your prognosis*	*Fulfilling dreams*
Completing projects	*Focusing on your faith*	*Other*

26 How might you react to a terminal prognosis?

Deny　　　　*Accept*　　　　*Fight*　　　　*Depends*

27   If you were to have a chronic, terminal illness, how do you think you would endure the pain?

In silence   Talk about it   Meditate it   Depends

28   If you were dying, would you want children under 10 to visit you?

No   Yes

Next Steps

Once you have completed your death awareness questionnaire, read over your answers.

What comes to mind when you see your answers? Did certain feelings arise, are there new concerns, do you feel prepared for your death, are there areas you want to learn more about?

Take note of these! Create tasks for each of your discoveries & you are on your journey to becoming more self-aware and have taken action for your rights and wishes!

The Dying Person's Bill of Rights

I have the right to be treated as a living human being until I die.

I have the right to maintain a sense of hopefulness, however changing my focus may be.

I have the right to be cared for by those who can maintain a sense of hopefulness, however changing this may be.

I have the right to express my feelings and emotions about my approaching death in my own way.

I have the right to participate in decisions concerning my case.

I have the right to expect continuing medical and nursing care even though "cure" goals must be changed into comfort goals.

I have the right not to die alone.

❋ *I have the right to be free from pain.*

❋ *I have the right to have my questions answered honestly.*

❋ *I have the right to not be deceived.*

❋ *I have the right to have help from and for my family in accepting my death.*

❋ *I have the right to die in peace and dignity.*

❋ *I have the right to retain my individuality and not be judged for my decisions, which may be contrary to those of others.*

❋ *I have the right to expect that the sanctity of the human body will be respected after death.*

❋ *I have the right to be cared for by sensitive, knowledgeable people who will attempt to understand my needs and be able to gain some satisfaction in helping me face my death.*

Building a Relationship with the Dying

There is not a step-by-step guide on how to form a relationship with someone. Rather, it is an individualized equation, which happens between two individuals and develops with the assistance of communication and respect. However, a great start to a relationship can come from "holding space" for an individual.

Holding space is when we are willing to walk alongside another person in whatever journey they are on without judging them, making them feel inadequate, trying to fix them, or trying to impact the outcome. When you hold space for other people, you open your heart, offer unconditional support, and let go of judgment and control.

To truly support people in their own growth, transformation, and grief, we cannot take their power away (fixing their problems) shaming them (implying they should know more than they do), or overwhelming them (giving more information than they are ready for). Rather, it is best to be prepared to step to the side and offer time for self-reflection and decision making, while offering unconditional love, support, and guidance when needed.

Many individuals have a deep-seeded fear or uncomfortableness around individuals at the end of life because they do not know what to do or say. However, sometimes you do not need to do or say anything! The most valuable thing you can do is just be there, be present, and be available for when an individual needs support and compassion. If you do encounter a conversation with an individual and you are unsure of what to say, know that you do not always need to be right or have the answer. Simply validating emotions, feelings, concerns, and providing phrases such as "that is hard", "I'm sorry", "what can I do?" can provide comfort.

COMMUNICATION TIPS

- *Validate feelings as "normal"*
- *Educate as much as requested*
- *Be non-judgmental*
- *Avoid clichés*
- *Speak from the heart/gut instinct*
- *Know your limits*
- *Be honest*
- *Don't be afraid to say "I don't know"*
- *Maintain balance/sense of humor when appropriate*
- *Acknowledge/validate rituals*
- *Listen*

Individuals with confusion, dementia, and conditions such as Alzheimer's, have progressive brain disorders that make it more and more difficult for them to remember, think clearly, communicate with others, or take care of themselves. These conditions can also interfere with their ability to control emotions and behaviors. Utilize communication "tools" for interactions, especially during difficult or frustrating situations.

Special Communication Tools:

Be Positive

Set a positive mood for interaction by using your attitude and body language. Use facial expressions and physical touch when appropriate to help convey your message and show a feeling of affection.

Get Attention

Get the person's attention and limit distractions when an activity needs to be completed, such as activities of daily living or changing. Always address them by their name, identify yourself by name, use nonverbal cues and physical touch to help maintain the focus. Eye contact is key!

Be Clear

Always use simple words and sentences, speak slowly, but in a distinct and reassuring tone. You will most likely need to repeat questions or statements; take a pause in between each to make sure you are getting your messageacross in the most accurate and clear way.

Ask Simple Questions

Yes or no questions work the best! Ask one question at a time and wait for a response, if they do not respond after a few minutes, ask again. If you cannot use a "yes/no" question, use a "choice" question, for example, "would you like to wear your white shirt or your blue shirt?"

Listen

Be patient in waiting for a response. Watch for nonverbal cues and body language to help guide your reaction or response. Always strive to listen for the meaning and feelings rather than the words.

Create Steps

Break down activities into a series of steps; this makes the task more manageable. Use visual cues often and slowly to help guide the steps.

Distract & Redirect

In the worst-case scenario, where the individual becomes upset or frustrated, try changing the subject or the environment. For instance, "I see you're feeling sad- I'm sorry you're upset. How about we go sit outside?".

Respond

When an individual is confused they may become anxious, unsure of themselves, confuse reality, and recall things that never really occurred. Avoid trying to convince them they are wrong. Stay focused on the feelings and body language at hand, provide emotional support and comfort, then gently redirect.

Remember

Remembering the past and sharing stories is often a soothing experience for individuals who are confused. Long-term memories are often the last to go, ask questions about their childhood or family to encourage socialization.

Maintain

Maintain calmness and a sense of humor whenever possible, though not at the individual's expense. Individuals who are confused typically retain social skills and are delighted to share in a laugh.

Comfort Measures for the Dying Person
Be Present

Being available for the individual physically and emotionally is being present. Be social with individuals, join them in watching TV or while having a meal at the kitchen table. Remind them that you are there for whatever they need, even if it is just someone to sit with them.

Quiet Presence

A quiet presence can be very powerful for a dying person, especially for those who are unresponsive. Just knowing someone is watching over you can bring relaxation and a sense of safety. While being a quiet presence you can provide gentle touch or listen to music. Before entering into silence let the individual know you are there as to not startle them.

Listen

Active listening is a powerful tool. When listening to a dying person or their loved ones, let them know you are active listening by shaking your head, leaning in, mimicking posture, and engaging in discussion when appropriate. Remember, when you are listening, you do not always need to have an answer or provide advice.

Engage

Engage in conversation anytime you can! Most individuals at the end of life enjoy talking about their life and memories, this can add to them feeling like their legacy will live on. Startup a conversation about the weather, their likes/dislikes, family, etc. Keep in mind some individuals may become tired during a conversation, gently acknowledge and ask them if they would like to rest or be alone.

Gentle Touch

A gentle touch like holding a hand or stroking a forehead can be calming for a dying person, especially if they are unresponsive. We all need human contact to help us feel better sometimes. Giving a back massage, hand massage, or arm massage with lotion can bring comfort as well. Pay attention to body language, if they clench their teeth or grimace they most likely are in pain or no longer want to be touched.

Music & Reading

Music can often be comforting to a dying person, play soft soothing sounds, their favorite music, or even sing. Reading books or the newspaper can bring a sense of calm as well to those who are active readers.

Religious Traditions

If it is appropriate to the individual, praying silently or reading passages from the bible can be calming and provide a sense of preparedness. Providing religious items to hold such as holy water or a rosary can help provide comfort in times of need.

Emotional Support

Being a support system for a dying person and their family is just as important as providing bedside care. Listen to them, let them know what they mean to you and others. Encourage the family to say good-bye and let go if they are able, this can give closure to a dying person, especially when they are close to passing. Let the family and individual know what you are going to do when entering the room and providing care. Offer family food or drinks as a welcoming gesture to make them feel more comfortable and taken care of during times of need.

Care for the Caregiver

Self-care is any activity that we deliberately partake in to take care of our mental, emotional, and physical health. Although it is a simple concept, in theory, it is something we often overlook. Successful self-care is key to improved mood and reduced anxiety. It is also key to a thriving relationship with oneself and others.

Providing care to individuals at the end of life can be both gratifying and frustrating. You are helping an individual, but at the same time watching the dying process, which can be sad and difficult. In order to avoid burnout, compassion fatigue, or extensive stress, you must know how to take care of yourself. After all, you cannot pour from an empty cup! Every individual's needs are different, therefore you must become self-aware to understand what type of self-care you may need and begin practicing it.

Practicing Self-Care

Self-care looks different for each individual, but all self-care should include a physical and psychosocial (social & emotional) component. It may take a few tries and different methods until you find a self-care activity that works for you; once you find it, make sure to practice it routinely (daily, weekly, monthly). While practicing self-care, be aware of what you are doing, why you are doing it, how it feels, and what the outcomes will be. If you are not completing an activity for the purpose of self-care and the positive outcomes become less prominent, it is time to consider a different method of practice that serves you more intentionally.

SUGGESTIONS FOR SELF CARE

- *Take a short walk*
- *Focus on your breathing*
- *Hydrate with water or a warm cup of tea*
- *Write down five things you are grateful for*
- *Stretch for five minutes*
- *Listen to your favorite song*

- *Turn your phone off, when you can*
- *Call a loved one or friend to chat*
- *Prepare or order a healthy meal*
- *Take a hot bath or shower*

Volunteering
⁂

The Joan Nicole Prince Home (JNP) is a 501(c)(3) non-profit that provides bedside care to two terminally ill individuals at the end of life, free of charge. The Home is run independently under Schenectady Community Home Inc., the Home is not a medical facility, and aims to provide an alternative treatment setting for individuals in their final days. The Home provides bedside care in a home-like environment, with individual bedrooms, bathrooms, a laundry room, kitchen, living room, and spacious backyard. In addition to services provided by the local Hospice organization, trained volunteers and staff provide 24/7 personal bedside care to residents. Volunteers also complete basic everyday tasks such as laundry, meal preparation, and cleaning, all while becoming "surrogate families" and providing emotional support to residents and their loved ones.

Become a volunteer by visiting our website, www.joannicoleprincehome.org/volunteer.

Donating
※

The Joan Nicole Prince Home is an IRS-recognized 501(c)(3) non-profit organization and relies solely on donations, community support, and grants for funding. The Home does not receive Medicare, Medicaid insurance reimbursement, nor any state or federal funding. Donations change the lives of the 12-18 residents served each year, along with their families and loved ones. Donations are tax-deductible and allow us to care for the terminally ill who have the greatest need and the fewest options at their end of life. Donations can be made to our Wish List, General Operations, Meditation Garden Brick Paver Campaign, and Planned Giving Campaign.

Donate today by visiting our website at, www.joannicoleprincehome.org/donate.

ACKNOWLEDGEMENTS:

Our team would like to thank all who have brought our mission into their hearts. Foremost, we wish to thank every resident and family member whom we have had the privilege of serving. Our time with you is filled with joy, love, sadness, and pain. We are honored to have known you and will forever hold space for you in our hearts. You have taught us all how to live for the moment, how to celebrate life, and how to love.

We are forever grateful to our founders who fought, created, and established our beautiful Home out of the kindness of their hearts and love for our community. Without their vision and dedication 15 years ago, we would not be where we are today. To our Board of Directors, Staff members, and subcontractors (both past and present), we are humbled by your gifts, generosity, and commitment to our Home. We have spent countless hours working towards the security and success of our Home together and we are in awe of your dedication to our mission.

We are thankful for all of our community partners and local higher education institutions including The Community Hospice, 1st National Bank of Scotia, All Seasons Equipment,

Amedore Builders. Bellamy Construction, Bennett Contracting, Dee's Kids, Dick and Betsy DeVos Foundation, Eastern Parkway UMC, Edgar and Elsa Prince Foundation, Fenimore Asset Management, First Reformed Churches, FPI Mechanical, General Electric, Habitat For Humanity of Schenectady County, Albany College of Pharmacy and Health Sciences, Albany Medical College, Maria College, SPH School of Nursing, Russell Sage College, Sage Colleges of Albany, SCCC, Skidmore College, SUNY Albany, The College of St. Rose, and Union College.

We would like to give a special thank you to Carol Weisse and the C.A.R.E Fellowship program. Your vision of education on end of life, compassionate care has grown right before our eyes and we are truly grateful for your guidance and to be on this journey with you.

We would like to thank those who have contributed to the completion of this book. To all the staff, volunteers, students, and family members who provided and trusted us with their stories and testimonies of our Home, we are truly honored to know you.

Most gratefully we wish to thank every volunteer who has stepped foot into our Home. You are the backbone, the blood, and strength of our mission and Home. With your time and dedication, our Home has remained a beautiful, welcoming, and joyful place. With your kindness and generosity, hundreds of terminally ill individuals and their families have found peace, compassion, and comfort in their final days. You have all shown us the true meaning of community and kindness.